ACKNOWLEDGEMENTS

As Cajuns, we live a very good life here in Louisiana, but this has come only after we paid our dues. In the 30's and 40's, we were considered to be something that had crawled out of the deep swamp. People even thought we had webbed feet.

Today, people from all over the world come to Louisiana to share our way of life and enjoy our festivals and good food. Thank God we now have things going our way. We passed very close to loosing it, cher! Prominent men like Cousin Dud, Roy Theriot and Mr. Domengeaux, to name a few, made us aware of our unique heritage. They gave us good reasons why we should preserve and protect it. They also gave us good reason to be proud to be Cajuns.

Sincerely Yours,

John Bergeron

D1235433

1

THE CAMEL RIDE

Tibodeau and Boudreau went way over there
to Egypt to see the pyramids and ride on a
camel. They went to a camel herder and rented
a camel for a day. The man took their ten
dollars and gave them their first riding
lesson. After they had gotten aboard the
animal, he gave them the reins. In order to
make the camel go, he told them the key
control words to make it stop and go. The man
told them to say the work "Keah" to get the
camel going. To go faster they were to say,
"Keah, Keah!" and the camel would gallop;
three times and the camel would go as fast as
it could. Tibodeau ask the man how to make
the camel stop. The man told him to say
simply "Amen."

Well, away they went over one dune and down
the other. Soon they got to a ravine; the
camel was still running wide open. As they
approached the abyss and the valley far below,
Boudreau asked Tibodeau what the word was to
make the camel stop. He didn't know.
Couldn't remember. Tib started praying and
when he finished, he said "Amen." The camel
stopped on a dime, right on the edge.
Boudreau was so glad he yelled out that famous
Cajun word one more time, "Keah!"

THE ELEPHANT HUNT

Boudreau and Tibodeau went all the way to
Africa to do some elephant hunting. They had
to return home on the first day over there.
They both got ruptured carrying the decoys.

BOUDREAU & CLARENCE, THE FEUDING TWOSOME

It seemed that Boudreau and Clarence were accustomed to having heated arguments daily on Bayou LaFourche. They would stand on each side of the Bayou and cuss and threaten, but they never ventured to cross during an argument.

Before long, the whole picture changed when an oil company started building a bridge to cross the Bayou next door to Boudreau and Tibodeau's house. Well, the day the bridge was completed the feuding twosome had one hell of an argument. Boudreau came in to eat dinner. He told Clotile he had enough of Clarence. After his lunch he stormed out of the door to whip his butt once and for all. He had taken enough! Out of the door he went, shaking with anger. Clotile watched him walk almost across the bridge then abruptly turn around and come back to the house as fast as he could.

"What is the matter, chere? I thought you was gonna go over there to beat him up?"

"That's true, Clotile, I was sure gonna do that, but I gotta tol' you I got scared, me. All the time I looked at Clarence from this side the Bayou he looked like a 'lil man. Mais, when I got almost across that bridge, I glanced up and there was a big sign there what said, 'Clarence 10 feet,' so I ran back before he saw me coming!"

CHICKEN JAMBALAYA

—1 large fryer (3 to 4 pounds), cut up
—2 tablespoons of salt
—½ teaspoon of red pepper
—4 tablespoons of oil
—½ cup of chopped celery
—½ cup of chopped bellpepper
—1 large onion, chopped
—½ cup of green onion, chopped
—4 cups of water
—2 cups of raw rice
—1 garlic clove, minced

1. Season chicken with salt and pepper; brown chicken in oil in a large heavy pot over medium heat. Set chicken aside.
2. Saute celery, bellpepper, onion and green onion in the same heavy pot until wilted, but not brown.
3. Add water, rice, chicken and garlic; mix well. Cover and cook on low heat until rice is done, about 30 minutes.

Shrimp and Oyster Jambalaya (au Bayou)

3   cups raw rice (washed)
½   pint oysters
1   clove garlic
¼   cup bell pepper
¼   cup cooking oil
1   bay leaf
1   tablespoon butter
    Chef-Magic Kitchen Seasoning
1   teaspoon Trappey's Worcestershire
    Sauce

1   lb. shrimp
1   large onion
½   cup celery
½   cup whole tomatoes
¼   cup flour
    salt to taste

Make a roux by letting cooking oil get real hot (see Roux page 13). Put in flour, stir until golden brown. Put in about ¾ of the onion, all celery and sauté until soft and wilt. Add tomatoes. Cook again 5 minutes. Set aside. Before this, boil about ¼ lb. shrimp 10 minutes. Use liquid from oysters also from boiled shrimp. Wash rice well and cook in these liquids until grains are tender. Now add to Roux that was set aside. To get the delicate flavor and tender qualities of shrimp and oysters cook ¼ of the onions and garlic in butter a few minutes. Put in shrimp for about 5 minutes and oysters 2 minutes. Pour mixture into rice mixture, stir well and heat a few minutes. Just before serving put Worcestershire sauce and parsley. Put in a covered tureen. Surround top of dressing with sprigs of parsley and ¼ lb. boiled shrimp. Chef-Magic Kitchen Seasoning will improve flavor a great deal. Mexi-Pep will add a delightful pepper tang.

a Cajun MOTOCYCLE

1991 © JB

J.Bergeron

COW-A-SOCKY

THE DOBERMAN DEPUTY

One day Sheriff Boudreau in Houma ran an ad in the paper what said, "One Deputy wanted right away!" The following day three cajuns and one Doberman Pincher showed up to apply for the job. The sheriff put them in a room and gave them a written test. Guess what? The doberman dog came out first!

Sheriff Boudreau sat in his office checking the results carefully. "I have a dope dog on the force already. I don't need another dog. What I need is one good strong man to fill the deputy job," he mulled. He brought the dog to his office, determined to find a way to get rid of it.

He looked the dog in the eye saying, "I have three more qualifications for you. I need for the deputy to be able to type. Can you do that?" The dog hopped up on a chair in front of the typewriter and began typing. It blew Boudreau's mind. " I need someone to be able to do work on a computer." The dog went over to the computer and began working on it.

"Dam!" Boudreau muttered. "Now, what can I do?" He thought a while and, at last, he knew he had a way to get rid of the dog. "Last, but not least, my new deputy must talk two languages." The dog looked Boudreau square in the eye and said "Meow."

THE BABY MACKEREL

Marie decided to go to see Doctor Mayeaux last week. She had been having problems getting pregnant so she made Tibodeau drive her 'dere on Wednesday to make sure the doctor had time to do a good job before the weekend. Well, she went in 'dat 'lil room 'dere and lay herself down and wait. Mais, in 30 or 25 minutes the good doctor came and check her out real good. After the examination he sat her down in his office and told her she didn't have cancer, she wasn't pregnant but she definitely had a fistula in her uterus, and it would be a miracle if she had a baby.

After that, she paid the receptionist and hurried to the truck to meet Tibodeau. When she sat down next to him she was shaking all over. He look at her face and she was white like a ghost.

"Mais, what the doctor told you, Marie? It mus' have scare you plumb, anh?"

"The doctor tol' me I had a fish in my uterus and if I get pregnant and have a baby, mais, it would be a mackerel fo' sho'!"

Fish Fillets Louisiane

1 ½ pounds fish fillets
Melted butter or margarine
2 tablespoons Spice-Up Table Seasoning
2 tomatoes, peeled and diced
¾ cup grated Parmesan cheese
Salt
Pepper
1 tablespoon grated onion

Place fish fillets on greased broiler pan. Brush generously with melted butter. Sprinkle with salt, pepper, Spice-Up Table Seasoning and grated onion. Scatter tomatoes evenly over fish. Place pan 4 inches from heat and broil for 18 to 20 minutes or until fish flakes easily when tested with a fork. Sprinkle cheese over fish and broil for 3 minutes or until cheese melts and browns.

OYSTER STEW

1 pt. oysters	1 1/2 tsp. salt
4 Tbsp. butter	1/8 tsp. white pepper
1 qt. milk	paprika to taste

Melt butter. Add drained oysters; cook about 3 minutes or until edges curl. Add milk slowly and stir while adding. Add salt and pepper. Bring almost to boiling point but do not let boil. Garnish with paprika. Serve hot.

11

CLOTILE'S SECRET STASH

Clotile and Boudreau had been married for 35 years and during this time Clotile had a small box tucked away under her bed. From the beginning, she had told Boudreau never to touch or look into her private box. It was hers and hers alone.

Well, it pained him very much and also worked on his mind. What in the world was in there? Why the big secret?

Poo Yaille! What was poor Boudreau to do? One day Clotile went to Wal Mart to buy some new coffee cups. She had just left when Boudreau went to her room, got on all fours and froze in front of the box like a bird dog pointing at a covey of quail. He put the box on the bed and cautiously opened it. Voila! Inside the box were six eggs and $1,000 cash. Satisfied at seeing nothing dramatic, he was about to close the lid when in walked Clotile.

"Boudreau, I tol' you not to touch 'dat! What you tink you doing, anh? "Dam to hell, you!"

"Mais, Clotile, I'm very sorry. Please excuse me. It's just 'dat for 35 years I tought about that dam box an' I couldn't stand 'dat anymore. I promise never to touch it again. But tell me Clotile, what mean those six eggs and all 'dat money?"

"Well, Boudreau, I take pity on you, so, I gonna tol' you what 'dat means. See 'doze six eggs --- mais, 'dat's the times you was not too good in the bedroom."

Boudreau tought to hisself "Hmm... six times in 35 years," and mentally was patting hisself on 'de back. What is 'de $1,000 for, I gotta know 'dat, too?"

"Well, sha...'dat $1,000 is the money I have left on all 'doze eggs I sold.

TO CATCH A BEAR

One day there was a black bear loose near Tibodeau's camp at Bayou Benoit. It climbed up a mulberry tree and wouldn't leave. Boudreau drove by and saw the people and Tibodeau standing a safe distance away looking up at something in the tree. When Tibodeau saw Boudreau coming he ran to meet his buddy saying, "There is a big bear in my mulberry tree. What I'm gonna do? It won't come down!"

"Don't worry 'bout 'dat Tib, I can get him down. I'll go home and get my gun, my stick and handcuffs and 'Ole Blue.'"

Boudreau returned with all three things. He walked up to the tree and asked Tibodeau to help him. "What you gonna do wit' 'doze 'tings, anh?" Boudreau told him he would climb up there next to the bear and poke him. When the bear lets go, he will fall to the ground. Ole Blue, the two-tooth dog, will lock on to his crotch and when the bear puts his paws on the dog's head, handcuff the bear, and we capture him.

I don't understand, then why you have 'de gun wit' that buckshot?"

"Well, if the bear knocks me down instead, be sure to shoot Ole Blue before I hit the ground."

FRIED ALLIGATOR

1 pound alligator meat sliced thin
1 (12 ounce) can beer
½ cup flour
1 teaspoon season-all
1 teaspoon salt
1 teaspoon pepper
Corn meal to dredge
Oil for frying

Make batter by combining beer, flour, season-all, salt, and pepper. Coat alligator meat with batter and dredge with corn meal. Fry in hot oil for about 15 minutes. turning often, until golden brown.

ONE DAY AT THE CASINO

Cajuns get together and play cards on weekends, so a little gambling is customary. When Boudreau and Tibodeau heard about that big place in Avoyelles where they could do all kinds of gambling and eat, too, they just had to check it out. Away they went with each $50 in their pockets. After they got inside, they got separated in that big place there. In an hour or two, Boudreau had spent his last dollar in the slot machines; luck was just not on his side. Mais, he started looking for Tibodeau, and he tried to whistle and call his name, but the noise in that place was too much for his poor 'lil whistle to be heard. He began looking for Tibodeau, and he found him in the restaurant eating a big hambug.

"Why you didn't buy you something else; there is so many good food in here?"

"Mais, hambug is what I like an' I got me one. Talk about good, too!"

"O.K., O.K. -- mais, how you did? You won?" He saw the big paper bag on the counter next to Tibodeau.

"Mais, I guess so! Me, I find a machine in there what give me four quarters back every time I put a dollar in it. Look all the money I got! I never loss one time!"

CRAWFISH ETOUFFEE

1 lb. crawfish, with fat
1 stick butter
2 cups chopped onion
½ teaspoon garlic powder
½ cup minced parsley
1 cup chicken broth
3 tablespoons browned flour
½ cup chopped green onion tops
Salt; black, red and white pepper to taste

Saute onion in butter until tender. Sift in flour, add fat and broth. Simmer slowly, covered, about 30 minutes. Add crawfish, salt and peppers and simmer another 15 minutes. Add green onions and parsley and simmer about 2 to 3 minutes. Serve over rice.

If gravy is too thick, add a little broth.

WILD GOOSE JAMBALAYA

1 goose
1 chopped onion
1 chopped bell pepper
½ cup chopped green onion
¼ cup chopped parsley
2 cups water
3 cups cooked rice
Salt and pepper to taste

Bake goose in oven until meat comes off the bones. Boil onion, bell pepper, green onions and parsley in water till tender. Take goose out of pan, take meat off the bones and cut in small pieces. Add onions. Bring mixture to running boil for a few minutes. Add meat and rice. Cook a few minutes on a low heat. Serves 4.

THE SPELLING LESSON

One day Tibodeau told Boudreau that he was going to the trade school to make hisself smart. He came home the first afternoon with a 'lil homework. The teacher told them to go to 'de dictionary and look up ten new words. One of the words on the list was "Propaganda.": He asked Boudreau what 'dat meant and Boudreau said, "Let me see now how I can 'splain that for you to understand." "Tib," he axed, "how many kids you got?" Tib replied, "Five, four daughters and one 'lil boy."

"They all look alike or like your family?"

"'De girls look all alike, but 'dat boy, I don't know who he look like."

"Well, that's what I mean -- 'doze girls all look like 'dey come from 'de proper goose-- but you see -- on 'dat last one there, you not the proper gander!"

ROAST WILD DUCK WITH ORANGE SAUCE

1 wild duck, dressed and
   cleaned
Slices of apple
Slices of onion

Celery slices
Dash of salt and pepper
2 thin slices salt pork

Inside the duck cavity, put the apple, onion and celery slices. Truss. Sprinkle with salt and pepper. Place salt pork strips over the breast. Bake at 400 degrees F for 30 minutes or until tender. When done, remove the apple, onion and celery from the cavity. Set duck aside to keep warm while preparing the sauce.

Sauce:
3 oranges
½ cup beef stock or 1 beef
   bouillon cube in ½ cup
   boiling water

½ cup white wine, vermouth
   or orange juice
1 tsp. cornstarch

Peel and quarter two of the oranges. Remove white inner pulp from the peel and cut peel into very tiny thin strips to make 1 full tablespoon. Place strips of peel, beef stock and wine or juice from orange quarters in small saucepan. Bring to a boil. Add cornstarch to enough cold water to make a paste. Add paste to hot stock to thicken slightly. Pour sauce over duck and garnish with unpeeled thin orange slices from the third orange. Serves 4.

JOHN WAYNE TOILET PAPER

Tante Tut-Tut live way far back of Grand Mare' there and she never went to 'doze big supermarkets to buy before. She got in that place and it 'mos took her breath away. She didn't know there was so many things to buy in this whole world. Her and Emile had been on corn cobs so long, she wanted to try some of that "toilet paper" before she die. She got one of the stock clerks to take her to that department, and there was so many kind to choose. She ax the young stock boy to recommend a good kind. He told her that the top shelf had the premium -- or most expensive kinds. The middle shelf had the medium brands -- good, but not that expensive. And finally on the bottom shelf -- that had the generic brands in the yellow bags. She ax the boy what that "generic" meant. The boy say to her, "That is the lowest price paper we got. They don't put nobody's name on that." Well. she bought a dozen rolls of that and had Emile drive her home. She try that paper there, and the next day when she was at her daughter's, she ax her to call that big store. She wanted to talk to the same boy what sold her the toilet paper. Soon he came to the phone and she began to tell him a few things, then she came to the point. "Tee boy," she say, " you know that paper what I bought, well, I got a good name for 'dat. Tell the company they should call it 'John Wayne'. The reason I call it 'dat is because it is rough and tough and it sho' don' take no crap off nobody!"

JOHN
WAYNE

© John Bergeron
1997

21

THE NEW YORK TRIP

Boudreau from Grand Coteau was soon going to take a trip to New York City, so everybody was talking about it. The day before he left, the old Mrs. Dunne, who lived up the road, passed at Boudreau's house to ax him to do a small favor for her up there. She told him that her son, John Dunne had moved up there 13 years ago. She had not heard a word from him since.

"Please Boudreau, if you would look for my son and if you find him, have him call his mama."

"I'm sure gonna do 'dat for you, Mrs. Dunne. I can promise you for sure--I will!"

Soon after getting to New York City he began trying to fulfill his promise. He look all over that big city for John and didn't have any luck until the last day before he left. He glanced up and look up at the front of a tall building. There, plumb across the front -- a big sign say "Dunne and Bradstreet." He was so glad for 'dat. He went into the front door and saw a nice 'lil lady sitting at a desk in one of those offices.

"Mam," he say to her, "you got a John in here?"

"Yes," that lady say, "go down that hall right there, the third door on the right.

As Boudreau walked up to the door, a freshly relieved man walked out. Boudreau ax him, "Are you Dunne?" The man answered him, "Yes, I'm done. Why you axing?" Boudreau say right back, "Mais, go to the phone and call your mama."

MARIE'S DEER HUNT

Marie had been wanting some fresh deer sausage for a long time. When the deer season opened, she axed Tibodeau to go catch one. To make sure he brought one back she told him she was going, too! Tib knew when she made her mind up about something--no use he try to change her mind. He grabbed his deer rifle and brought the automatic 22 rifle for her, and away they went to the lease.

He put her in a blind and walked over to his, a little further down. Before he got there, he hear Marie shoot her rifle and then he heard her screaming. He turned around an' ran over to where she was. When he got close, he saw a man with his hands in the air saying, "O.K., lady! It's your deer--but, would you mind if I took my saddle off it."

VENISON STEW
(Brady Style)

—Salt
—Pepper
—2 pounds of venison, cut in 2-inch squares, ¼-inch thick
—Flour
—¼ cup of melted butter
—½ cup of chopped bellpepper
—1 cup of chopped celery
—1 can of sliced mushrooms (2 ounces)
—1 can of cream of mushroom soup
—1 small can of brown mushroom gravy
—Minced parsley

1. Salt and pepper venison squares and cover with seasoned flour; fry quickly in melted butter. Remove venison and set aside.
2. In drippings, saute bellpepper and celery; then add venison, mushrooms, soup and gravy. Check for seasoning, using red pepper and black pepper and salt. If color is not as dark as you like it, add a little Kitchen Bouquet. Cook until tender. Sprinkle with minced parsley before serving over hot rice.

© '97
J.W.B.

24

THE VETERINARY VISIT

A while back, Boudreau's dog "Ole Blue" got something wrong with him. He would just lie down, hardly breathing. Besides that, he quit eating and wouldn't even wag his tail no more. Tib loved "Ole Blue" so he put him in the pick 'em up and brought him to see the vet -- Prejean, on Friday. He was worried plumb out of his mind for "Ole Blue". He told the Doc all the things "Ole Blue" wasn't doing anymore. Doc Prejean put the dog on a table in his back office and began looking at the dog all over. As he would walk around and touch the dog, he would say, "Hm, on hon." Once in a while he would say, "Yep, on hon." "Boudreau, I'm gonna give him a B-12 shot for good measure."

After the shot, he called Fe Fe, his big persian cat into the room. He put him on the table and he jumped on Ole Blue's head. The cat scratched and clawed, but the poor dog was no longer breathing. He never moved a muscle. The cat stopped after that and smell him and finally jumped down and went in the other room. Doc told Boudreau to follow him to the front office. Doc sat down and started writing him a bill for his service. When he finished writing, he handed Boudreau the bill. The bill showed "$500 total due for services rendered." "$500! screamed Boudreau. "But you only gave Ole Blue one shot. That can't be that expensive, anh?"

"Well, it was $25 for the B-12 shot and the visit and $475 for the cat scan."

THE BEST OF BOTH WORLDS

One day Boudreau was over at the Cypress having a couple of beers, and talking to Mac and Vic. After having a few drinks together, they left and Boudreau was alone except for the barmaid. He and the barmaid began talking about this and that. Out of curiosity he axed the beautiful barmaid what men she thought was the best lovers. She thought a while and replied, "Mais, as far as I know, the American Indian Braves and the Louisiana Cajuns were the best because of the kinds of peppers they eat. It was definitely due to something in their diet."

"That is very interesting," Boudreau said. I didn't realize that until today. I am so glad you shared that information with me." Soon, the barmaid say, "By the way, what is your full name, Boudreau?"

"Mais, cher--I'm so glad you tought to ax me 'dat! My front and back name is Sitting Bull Boudreau."

BROKEN HEARTED

Boudreau found one of his good friends, Picou getting plastered out of his mind at the local bar in Delcambre last Saturday. He was drinking heavy with two or three beers in front of him all the time. Boudreau see that and he went over there and ax him what was wrong. He looked so bad.

What's the matter, Picou? Why you get drunk like that?" Picou look at him and say, "My wife left me for my best friend." He downed another beer, and with tearful eyes he say, "An' I miss him so much!"

1897© John Bergeron

SMOTHERED QUAIL

—½ cup of cubed bacon
—Salt and pepper
—8 quails
—6 tablespoons of flour
—1 medium onion, chopped
—2½ cups of canned chicken broth
—Pinch of thyme
—½ bay leaf
—1 tablespoon of parsley, chopped

1. Saute bacon until brown and remove from skillet.
2. Put lightly peppered and salted quail in drippings and when browned, remove; add flour and onions, and stir a minute.
3. Add all ingredients and return bacon and quail to gravy; cover and simmer 20 to 30 minutes, turning occasionally until done. Add more chicken broth if needed.
Serve with white rice.

29

THE HOSPITAL VISIT

Tante MiMi went to the hospital last week to get operated on her toe. She didn't have many visitors so Tibodeau decided to go see her. She was his only aunt and she liked him so much. He asked for her room number at the reception desk. She told him to get on de alligator and ride to the fourt floor. She was in room 410 on the right side of the alligator. He found his way with no problems. He got in the room and he gave her a 'lil flower he had picked outside. She was so glad to see him, an' she began talking and talking and it made Tibodeau so nervous he start chewing his fingernails. Then he noticed a small bowl on the table by the bed that was full of peanuts. He grabbed a handful and started eating. When he got through wit' dat, he grabbed some more and ate them, too! Mais, that was some good peanuts, yea! He ate all there was in the bowl as MiMi talked and talked her head off. She was so glad to see him. Soon, he stop her for a minute and he say to her, "Poo yaille! look what I did. I ate all your peanuts. I'll go buy you some more."

"Oh, no, chere. It's O.K., I was gonna throw 'doze away. I can't chew 'de peanuts without my teeth, so I suck 'de chocolate off and put 'de peanuts in 'de bowl."

TURTLE, ALLIGATOR OR CHICKEN SAUCE PIQUANTE

2 cooking spoons flour (for roux)
   Cooking oil (for roux)
⅓ cup shallots, chopped
6 cloves garlic, chopped
½ cup sugar
2 qts. Hunt's tomato sauce
   Ground bay leaves (optional)
1 cup celery, chopped
3 lbs. meat of choice
1 cup onion, chopped
½ cup bell pepper, chopped
⅓ cup parsley, chopped
1 pint stuffed olives
2 pints mushrooms
   Salt, black and red pepper to taste

1. Make a roux with flour and oil.

2. Add tomato sauce, celery, onion, bell pepper, shallots, garlic, sugar, ground bay leaves and cook for 3 hours.

3. Add seasoned meat of choice (turtle, chicken or alligator) to tomato sauce. Cook for 1 or 2 hours or until meat is tender, but not falling off bones.

4. One-half hour before meat is tender, add parsley, olives and mushrooms.

5. Season to taste with salt and the peppers. Serve over rice.
   Serves 15

Blackened Redfish

A unique presentation from Cajun country. Herbs and spices are seared onto the flesh with very high heat, cooking it quickly.

2 pounds Redfish fillets, 1/2-3/4 in. thick
1 cup margarine or butter
1 tablespoon paprika
1 teaspoon salt
1 teaspoon onion powder
1 teaspoon garlic powder
3/4 teaspoon black pepper
3/4 teaspoon white pepper
1/2 teaspoon cayenne pepper
1/2 teaspoon dried thyme leaves
1/2 teaspoon dried oregano leaves

Mix all dry ingredients in a flat pan. Heat a large cast-iron skillet over high heat. Turn on hood vent. Do not use lighweight or nonstick skillet. Melt about 3 tablespoons margarine in skillet. Dip each fish portion in remaining margarine, then in the dry ingredients, patting them in by hand. Cook fish on each side for 2 to 3 minutes, being careful when turning. The fish will look charred. There will be some smoke, but not excessive. This recipe may be cooked outdoors if preferred. Makes 5 to 6 servings.

CORN PONES A LA AVOYELLES

−1½ cups of corn meal
−3 tablespoons of all-purpose flour
−1½ tablespoons of baking powder
−1 teaspoon of salt
−2/3 cup of hot water
−1½ cups of shortening

1. Mix all dry ingredients. Add in hot water, mixing well.
2. Immediately make patties.
3. Fry patties in deep, hot shortening until golden brown on each side.

Maison de Acadien
dans la Louisiane du sud

1995 J. Bergeron

BLACKENED CHICKEN BREAST

½ teaspoon paprika

⅛ teaspoon salt

¼ teaspoon ground red pepper

¼ teaspoon ground cumin

¼ teaspoon ground thyme

⅛ teaspoon ground white pepper

⅛ teaspoon onion powder

1 boneless chicken breast half, skinned

Preheat the oven to 350 degrees F. Heat a medium cast-iron skillet over high heat for 15 minutes, or until very hot. In a small bowl, combine all the dry seasonings; mix well and set aside.

Spray one side of the chicken with non-stick vegetable cooking spray and sprinkle with half the seasonings; reserve the remaining seasonings. Place the chicken in the very hot skillet, seasoned side down. Repeat procedure with top side of the chicken; cook for 1 minute on each side.

Remove the chicken from the skillet and place it on a small baking sheet that has been sprayed with non-stick vegetable cooking spray. Bake in a 350-degree F oven for 5 minutes.

Makes one serving.

Nutrition information per serving: 243 cal., 5 g fat, 120 mg chol., 350 mg sodium.

COME HELL OR HIGH WATER

In June or July it rains the most in South Louisiana. For a while it rain four or three inches every day. Boudreau had been playing cards and drinking his beer every day, and Clotile had been after him to mow 'de lawn for pass a week, maybe for two or so. She was getting plumb mad and when she did 'dat, you don't want to be around 'dat 'ting, no!

Well, one morning the weather look real good and Clotile laid the law to Boudreau, and then she went to visit her friend, Marie next door. After a while there was a big blue time come up and man, the rain began to pour down by the buckets full. The water in the yards kept rising higher and higher, and Marie suggest they climb up 'de roof to be safe. As they were sitting up there looking around at all 'dat water, Marie notice a straw hat on top 'de water. That hat act kind of like something was in the water under it. "Clotile, I'm getting scared of 'dat hat. What you believe 'dat is?" Clotile had been watching the hat do on the water too, but she was not scared her. She tol' Marie, "Don't worry about 'dat, you -- 'dat's just Boudreau mow 'de lawn him. Before I left, I tol' him to be dam sure to cut 'dat grass 'come hell or high water' and finally he listen to me!"

YOU'RE SMOTHERING ME!

SHRIMP ETOUFFEE

—2 large onions, chopped fine
—1 large bellpepper, chopped fine
—¼ pound of oleo
—2 pounds of shrimp, peeled and deveined
—Green onions
—Salt and pepper to taste

1. Saute onions and bellpepper in oleo until tender.
2. Stir in shrimp; cook at medium heat until shrimp are done. Add a small amount of water, as needed.
3. Add green onions; cook about five minutes. Season with salt and pepper. Serve over rice.

BOUDREAU AND THE POPE

As Boudreau and Tibodeau were jogging one morning, Boudreau told Tib he knew everybody around. Tib didn't believe him, so he told him to prove it.

O.K., this afternoon the Governor will be coming to Crowley to visit his mamma. You can come with me and see for yourself. Sure enuf--when the governor drove up, Boudreau got out and hollered to him, "Hey Ed, my fren', how you been, anh?"

"Why, Boudreau, is that you? I haven't seen you in months. You been O,K.? The proof was in the pudding--the Governor knew him. Tib needed some more proof. "Who else you know that's famous?" "Well, I'm good friends with Fats Domino. He will be at the Airport Club in Abbeville Saturday nite. We'll go and hear him play and have a few beers, then you'll see when he arrives."

Saturday nite came and they went to the club. Sure enough, when Fats came in, he came over to their table and shook hands with Boudreau, saying--"Hey Boudreau, comment sa va?" (How are your doing?) "Mais, fine Fats, you gonna play my song after while?" He say, "You know it, my friend."

Tib was very impressed, but still wanted more proof. That summer in Rome, Boudreau and Tibodeau went to the Vatican. Boudreau told Tib he knew the Pope. "No you don't!" replied Tibodeau. Boudreau told Tib he would be right back, and went inside the building where the Pope was. Soon the crowd began cheering. In a window on the second floor two men appeared. The Pope and Boudreau! One of the guys standing next to Tibodeau told him, "I know the guy on the left, that's Boudreau, but who is the guy standing on the right?"

THE COSTUMED COW

The grade school in Raceland was having a play and required that somebody volunteer to put a cow suit on. Boudreau and Tibodeau had some 'lil kids in 'dat school so 'dey volunteered. The suit was in two parts; the front part with the head, shoulders and front legs. The back part consisted of the back, legs and tail. Tibodeau got in front since he was taller. Boudreau got in the back part since he had a belly and a round rump. As they walked across the pasture to the school, Tibodeau noticed a big black bull in the far corner.

"I hope 'dat big bull stays in 'dat corner over 'dere," Tibodeau tol' Boudreau.

"Mais, I can't see nothing back here so keep both you eyes on him and let me know if he's coming."

"So far, so good. He still has his head down eating grass. Oh, Oh! He's looking this way!"

They went a little further trying to get to the fence. The bull started walking in their direction. Then he started running toward them.

"What he's doing now, Tib?" By that time the bull was almost on them.

Tibodeau stuck his head under the fence and said, "Hey, Boud, I think you better brace yourself real good. That big black bull is coming fast and by the look in his eyes, I think he loves you!"

1997
© JWB John Bergeron

BOUDREAU AND THE TROOPER

One evening Boudreau was going to Crowley on I-10 from Lafayette. He was listening to his cajun music and minding his own business, when he glanced in his rear view mirror and saw the flashing lights on a trooper's car coming up behind him. Instead of pulling over and stopping, he push down that full speeder and tried to outrun the state trooper. He almost made it to Crowley when his car ran out of gas. He got out of his car with his hands in the air saying "Don't shoot!"

"Why did you try to outrun me?" the trooper asked him. "You didn't see my lights?"

"Well, officer, fifteen years ago my wife run away with a state trooper an' I thought you was that trooper coming to bring her back!"

TURTLE SOUP

1 medium size turtle	6 Tbsp. **shortening**
1 large onion, chopped	2 stalks celery, cut up
1 bay leaf	1 sprig thyme
1 green pepper, cut up	4 Tbsp. tomato paste
3 Tbsp. flour	1 qt. hot water
Salt and pepper to taste	1/2 c. wine -(sherry)
1 or 2 hard boiled eggs, sliced	1/2 lemon, sliced

Cut turtle meat in small pieces. Fry in shortening brown. Add onion, celery, bay leaf, thyme, green pepper, tomato paste, salt, pepper and flour.
all ingredients are mixed. Add hot water and simmer 1 - 1 1/2 hours. Remove from fire, add wine. Serve with slices of egg and lemon.

Clotile and Boudreau were fishing in Miller's Lake one day, and as they fished, Boudreau began to notice all those beer cans floating around the lake. They made the place look so bad. He began picking them up and putting them in the boat.

"Clotile, we can sell 'doze cans for lots of money when we get back!"

When his hand touched the fifth can -- "poof" -- a big genie popped out. Scared them both half to death. The genie told Boudreau he would grant him one wish and one alone.

"What is your wish? Speak now."

Boudreau thought a little while then he say, "Mr. Genie, I would like for you to turn all the water in this lake into beer."

Clotile shook her head and tried to stop the process which took place before her very eyes. Too late! The water turned to beer. The fish began swimming on the surface in circles. All drunk! Finally Clotile opened her mouth and spoke. "Boudreau," she said, "boy you mess up bad, Chere. I got to tol' you 'dat 'rite now. Every time you gonna make p.p., you gonna have to do 'dat in the boat from now on!"

SHRIMP AND CRAB DINNER

1 lb. raw shrimp
1 lb. crabmeat
1 can cream of mushroom soup
1 can cream of celery soup
1 c. tap water

1 c. raw rice
1 medium onion
1 stalk celery (2 or 3 pieces)
1 bell pepper
1 tsp. cooking oil

Mix shrimp, onion, pepper and celery and cook in pot for 15 minutes. Add crabmeat, mushroom and celery soups, water, rice and cooking oil. Mix well and bake in casserole dish for 1 hour at 350°.

ACUTE ANGINA

Years ago, Clotile took their daughter to Dr. Picou for an examination. The poor girl had been having chest pains and Clotile was worried for her. Well, years passed and Charlotte did real good with the pills the doctor had give her, and when she got 17 years old she fell in love with a boy from down Bayou Tigre. The poor girl didn't know if she should tell her boyfriend about her illness or not because he was getting pretty serious and wanted to marry her. Clotile told her it was no use to do 'dat; he might change his mind. Boudreau on the other hand was in the opinion that she should start the marriage on the right foot and tell the boy about her acute angina. "If you don't do 'dat, me--I'm gonna tell him 'de truth myself!"

Well, Charlotte didn't want to tell the boy anything for fear of losing him. So, on Friday night when the boy came to pick her up to go to Palombo's to the dance, Boudreau sat him down in the kitchen and they had a cup of coffee. "Tee-Boy, I want you to know before you marry Charlotte, she got acute angina!"

Well, Mr. Boudreau, I'm happy to know 'dat she got something good going for her 'cause she sure don't have anything on her chest, no!"

THE BIG BIRD

Quibodeau won a few thousand dollars in the scratch off lottery. He had always wanted to buy a motor driven hand glider, so now was his chance to buy one. He drove all the way to Lafayette to the dealer and bought one on Saturday. He knew that Boudreau and Tibodeau would be at their camp on the Chene, so after a few short lessons he decided to fly over there to show it to them. As he drew near, Boudreau saw that big bird-like thing coming in their direction. He told Tibodeau to keep an eye on it as he ran to the porch to get his shot gun. When he got back to the dock where Tibodeau was, the big thing with wings was almost overhead and was flying real low. He took careful aim and, "Ketow!" He let go with one loud blast. They looked at each other and back at the glider. Tibodeau told Boudreau, "You missed." He had just said that when a man started falling to the ground.

"Oh, no I didn't miss. Look that big bird let Quibodeau go! See him falling down. He's gonna fall in the Bayou."

CHRISTMAS GIFTS

It was the end of November and Tibodeau and Marie were sitting in the living room talking about Christmas. They were trying to decide what kind of gifts they would give to everybody. Before Tibodeau could tell Marie what kind of gift he wanted, she uttered the word "divorce!" "I want a divorce, Tib!"

Not missing a step or taking a deep breath, Tib calmly replied, "Mais, Marie, I was not planning to spend that much money on you this Christmas!"

TO ~~BUY~~ A BULL
BORROW

Boudreau and Tibodeau decided to get into the cattle business. They went out and bought 30 or 25 momma cows to start with and almost blew their entire stash. Every day they would sit out there in the shade of the barn and watch the cattle. Months passed and their herd didn't grow any larger. "Something is wrong!" Boudreau told Tibodeau. "I'm gonna go ax Hebert what he thinks is the matter." Hebert came by to look at the cows and right away he noticed the problem.

"Mais, I don't see a bull in that herd. Y'all gotta have a bull to make the herd grow."

Boudreau and Tibodeau didn't have enough money left to buy a bull, but Boudreau thought about his friend in Texas. He would get on the bus and go talk to him and see those bulls in person. He told Tibodeau he would send a telegram when the deal was made so that he could bring the trailer to pick it up. He got there and picked out a nice bull and his friend told him he would loan it to him for a few months.

Boudreau went to the telegraph office with his last $6.00 to tell Tibodeau what to do. He walked in the office and the lady behind the desk told him that the messages would cost $2.00 per word. Boudreau was all upset, because he still wanted to buy a hamburger and a coke. He tought a while and it came to him like a divine inspiration. He gave the lady $2.00 and told her to send just one word to Tibodeau in Lockport, LA. The word he handed her was "Comfortable." It didn't make any sense to her. "Send that word, please. Mah friend, Tibodeau don't spell too good, but he'll know what that word means, "com for ta bul!"

LENTEN PENANCES

Soon that time of the year came and Easter was coming, so it was time to do lenten penances. Tibodeau was the first to declare that he was gonna stop eating chocolate candy during lent. That was hard for him to do since his one weakness was chocolate candy. He saw Boudreau at the barber shop and told him of his penance. "Boudreau, what you gonna give up this time?" "Mais, let me 'tink a while. O.K, me, I'm gonna give up sleeping with Clotile. You know how I like 'dat. It's gonna be hard -- but, I can do it if you can."

A few weeks passed until Boudreau and Tibodeau met at the meat market. "Hello, there, Tib, my fren'. How you doing with your penance, you?" "Mais, Boudreau, I hate to say that -- mais, I broke my penance just one time. I passed by the store and saw some of 'doze chocolate candy in the window and I had to eat one or two pieces 'rite away. An' you, how you doing?"

"Like you, I broke my penance, too, a few days ago. That sweet woman just fill my eyes with desire, and I broke my penance, too."

"Well, what Clotile say about you breaking your penance? She was glad, yes?"

"Mais, no, she was not happy 'wit 'dat. She grab a bat and broke my head 'wit it."

"Keaw! Why she did that?"

"Mais, because I was at Winn Dixie at 'dat time and the woman what made me broke my penance was Placide's wife!"

BETTY CROCKER

Clotile had been asking Boudreau to do little chores around the house for a long time. She asked him to fix the door knob on the front door. He turned his face toward Clotile and said, "Do you see a sign on my forehead that says 'carpenter'?" and he walked away from her. That afternoon she asked him to check the light switch in the living room. He turned his face toward her, pointing to his brow, "Do you see a sign on my forehead saying 'electrician'?" and he walked away. She heard the car start up and he drove away to the local bar.

A few minutes later, Tibodeau dropped in to visit his buddy. Clotile was so upset with Boudreau. She told Tibodeau that she had asked him to fix the door knob and the light switch. Boudreau got mad and went to the bar to drink instead.

"I can fix 'doze things for you Clotile, but there will be a slight charge. I don't work for "free." You have two choices. The first is that you be "sweet" to me or you can bake me a cake for my trouble."

Well, when Boudreau got back, the door knob was fixed and so was the light switch. "Who fix 'doze things, you?" he asked. Mais non, not me! It was your friend Tibodeau what fix that."

"You had to give him something?"

"Yes, he gave me two choices--to make him some sha-sha or to bake him a cake."

"Mais, what you did, anh?"

"Well, Boudreau, you guess. Look at my forehead and tell me if it say Betty Crocker up 'dere!"

1997 John Bergeron

THE PIPELINE JOB

Our good welder friend, Boudreau went to California in his welding truck. When he got there, he stopped at a filling station to get directions and gas. One of the station attendants came out to clean his windshield. Boudreau, who was lost asked the man for directions to "El Cajon" California. Upon hearing the way Boudreau pronounced the word "Cajon" he asked where he was from. Boudreau told him he had come over from Louisiana to work on a pipeline. The attendant told him that in California, the letter "j" was pronounced like an "h." They continued talking together and the fellow asked Boudreau how long the pipeline job would last. Remembering what the fellow had told him, and trying to impress him with his ability to pick up on things, Boudreau told the guy, "Well, Neg, I think that job gonna last 'til 'Hune' or maybe 'Huly'!"

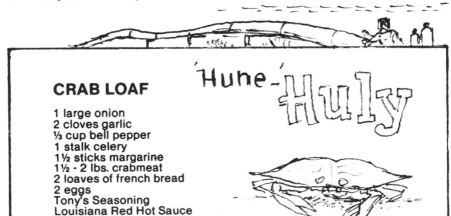

CRAB LOAF

'Hune-Huly'

1 large onion
2 cloves garlic
⅓ cup bell pepper
1 stalk celery
1½ sticks margarine
1½ - 2 lbs. crabmeat
2 loaves of french bread
2 eggs
Tony's Seasoning
Louisiana Red Hot Sauce
Salt and pepper

Chop and cook the first 4 ingredients in 1 stick of margarine until vegetables are fairly well cooked. Add crabmeat to this and cook until warmed. Hollow out loaves of french bread. Toast the part of the bread that has been removed from the loaves. Add this toasted bread to crab mixture. Add eggs and seasonings. Mix well. Place mixture in hollowed bread loaves. Wrap in tin foil and bake at 350° 8 - 10 minutes.

THE STUD OF HOLLY BEACH

Everybody know that around south Louisiana Boudreau is quite a ladies man. He lives in a 'lil shack on the beach. When he comes out with his baseball cap, cut offs and tenny shoes, 'de girls flock around him like cats around a fish cart. He was the stud of Holly Beach! One day he decided to go to California to make some big money to build him a nice camp back in Louisiana someday. Well, he found a good job as a street cleaner and that first weekend he put on his cut offs, cap and tenny shoes and headed for the beach. He paraded around like a peacock waiting for the girls to rush around him. He was "'de stud of Holly Beach." Nothing! The girls threw up their noses and walked away from him. Ug! what a creep--they thought. Something was very wrong! Women were the same all over. Why weren't they flocking to him like at Holly Beach? He walked over to the lifeguard station and axed the big life guard on duty to tell him what he was doing wrong.

The life guard looked him all over and told him he had to get rid of the tenny shoes, the cap and the cut offs. He must go to a swim shop and get a whole new outfit. Some wrap-around sunglasses, some nice beach shoes, some psychedelic nose cream and a skimpy skin tight bathing suit--and, also a big potato.

Well, the next day he purchased the things the lifeguard told him. He couldn't wait to hit the beach and pull those women to him like a magnet. When he saw some pretty ones coming, he turned sideways, flexed his muscles and hummed a 'lil cajun tune. Guess what? Those poor women ran away from him like he had the plague. Mais, Got dog! What was 'de matter? He did everything the lifeguard tol' him.

'97
©Bergeron

He ran over to the big lifeguard, almost in tears. Him--the stud of Holly Beach! They didn't want him at all! Keah! He was so hurt. "Why, Why? What's wrong wit' me?" "Show me how you presented yourself to them," the lifeguard said. Boudreau gave him the side view with the flexing muscle act. "You dumb cajun," he told Boudreau. Why you put the potato in the back end of your bathing suit like that?"

THE HELICOPTER RIDE

Not too long ago, Tibodeau went to Lafayette
and got hisself some helicopter lessons at the
airport. In no time at all, he had gotten
good at it.

One Saturday, Boudreau drove to the airport
to see Tibodeau in action. He saw how good
his friend was at flying the chopper--it got
to him. He didn't like anybody, especially
Tibodeau, to be better than he was in
anything. When Tibodeau landed, he went to
meet him at the helipad.

"Tib," he said, "you real good at that. You
think you can let me drive a 'lil so I can
show you what I can do?"

"Mais, if you think you can, I'll get out
and let you have the controls." Sure enough,
he did and he watched Boudreau get 'dat
chopper off the ground, and he just kept going
straight up. He went up passed the clouds and
still kept going up. What you believe he was
thinking to do that? He kept going up still
more and went almost out of sight. Not too
long pass, and he saw the chopper coming down
and down real fast--straight down! Soon came
a big bang as the chopper hit the ground--
wheels, blades, glass and metal flying
everywhere. 'Most flattened that thing! Out
of the wreckage, Boudreau walked out limping
and cussing.

"Mais, what happen, Boudreau? Did the motor
break?"

"No, Tib, it was me what make it stop. When
I got real high, it was cold up there and
those big propellers kept passing that cold
wind on me--so I jus' turn them off!

THE DEER HUNT

One winter morning Boudreau and Tibodeau went deer hunting. They got out of the pick 'em up, and before they went each a separate way, they agreed to firing two shots in case of an emergency or if help was needed. Away they went and soon Tibodeau kill a deer--a big buck. He needed help, so he fire two shots in the air--nothing! No Boudreau show up.

Meanwhile, on the other side the woods, Boudreau sat on a forked tree and started watching for a deer. First thing what happen was Mother Nature call him to make number 2. Well, he did 'dat, and as usual he fall asleep. Still sitting on the forked tree, he propped his head on a branch in front of him and took a nap.

By that time, Tibodeau had skin out the deer, cut off the rumps and the rib rack and headed back to the pick 'em up. He pass not far from where Boudreau was sleeping in that fork.

"I'm gonna fix him! He never gonna sleep after doing his business again." Tibodeau went back to the spot where he skin the deer and pick up the pile of guts. He put those guts under Boudreau as he slept. When he got 50 feet away, he say, "Hey, Boudreau! Wake up! I need your help! I kill me a big deer! Help me!"

Boudreau open his eyes, looked at Tibodeau as he walked toward the pick 'em up. He took a long time, but finally he got to the truck.

"What happen to you, Boud? Why you took so long?"

"Mais, Tib, man! I got ascared me! I did number 2 and I pass all my guts. Boy, that scare me, but I took care of 'dat. No problem! I find me a good strong stick an' I push them all back in."

VENISON ROAST

1 (4 lbs.) venison roast
½ cup vinegar
2 cloves garlic, chopped
2 Tbsps. salt
2 Tbsps. flour
Oil for browning

1 tsp. dry mustard
2 Tbsps. brown sugar
1 large onion, sliced
1 Tbsp. Worcestershire sauce
1 (10 oz.) can tomatoes with
   green chilies

Prepare marinade by combining vinegar, garlic, salt and enough cold water to cover roast. Pour over roast and marinate overnight in refrigerator. Pat dry. Roll in flour and brown in skillet. Place in slow cooker. Add remaining ingredients and cook on high for 2 hours. Turn to low and cook for 8-10 hours. 6-8 servings.

WORKING AT THE SPACE CENTER

One summer Boudreau and Tibodeau got a job at the Kennedy Space Center in Florida. They didn't know they were in a dry county, so they were in for hard times with no booze. Towards the end of the week they were getting pretty thirsty for a beer, but alas, they were out of luck! No alcohol on the premises--that is, for drinking purposes.

Boudreau was getting desperate, but he had a bright idea. "Go downstairs and get us two cans of Sprite in the pop machine, Tib. Don't ask why--jus' do it." Tib went downstairs for the pop and Boudreau went to the warehouse with a big coffee cup. He filled it with some 300 proof methyl alcohol--used for fuel in jet engines at the Center. He went back and met Tib at his work station. They each drank a few slugs of pop to make room in the cans, filling them back up. He grinned at Tib and told him to try some as he walked back to his room.

About thirty minutes passed and then the phone started ringing off the hook. After drinking his drink, Boudreau was not in the mood to talk on the phone. He let it ring a few times and finally answered. "Hello, who is it?"

The voice on the other end said, "Hey Boud, this is Tib. Did you drink your spirits yet?"

He said, "Yes, who is this?"

"This is Tib and I gotta ax if you went to the men's room yet?"

"No, me I didn't go yet."

"Well, don't poo when you go in 'dere 'cause I did--and I'm way out here in North Carolina?"

62

THE FRIDAY NIGHT GAMES

Boudreau and Tibodeau had been going to the basketball games at USL for many years. The only problem was they were never able to stay until the game was over due to the fact that they had to leave early so that they could find their car before everybody else got out. It troubled Boudreau, so he came up with a solution. Now, they would be able to stay 'til the end like everybody else.

Friday evening Tibodeau showed up, as usual, ready to go to the game. He and Boudreau walked out to the garage. Boudreau led Tibodeau around toward the back yard. "Hey, Neg, you lose your head or something? The car is in the garage!" "We not going in the car 'dis time," he said as they continued walking. "We gonna ride this thing," he said pointing to a camel tied to a tree. "You better catch your head!" Tibodeau retorted. "No, no, Tib, by going on a camel, we won't lose it in that bunch of cars. That way, we can watch all the game." Away they went to the game. They tied the camel to a tree near the parking area and went in to watch the game. They stayed until the last "poof" -- and walked out with everybody else, secure in the knowledge that this time they would be able to find their camel right away. "Mais, non!" When they got out and looked, there were 20 other camels on the lot. "Poo yaille!" Tibodeau exclaimed. "Don't worry about 'dat, you. Just pass me your flashlight," Boudreau retorted. He grabbed the flashlight, walked up to the first camel, raised its tail and looked back there. "Nope, not that one." He walked to the next one, raised the tail, put some light on the area. "Nope, not that one, either." Tibodeau stood there shaking his head. "How you gonna find our camel like that?" he asked. "Mais," Boudreau say, "you remember when we stopped at the red light on our way here? You remember that woman what stopped and stuck her head out the window...what she said?" Mais, she said, "Look at those two a - - holes on that camel!"

THE GENIE IN THE DRUM

One day Boudreau and Tibodeau were fishing in each their boats in the Basin Canal. Soon Boudreau see Tibodeau paddling toward him. When he got there he ax Boudreau to borrow his cigarette lighter. He wanted to smoke real bad and couldn't find his lighter.

"Hey, Boud - let me borrow your lighter. I can't find mine." Boudreau whipped out a pretty Bic lighter a foot long. Man, he pushed down on that lighter and a flame 6 inches tall came out. Tibodeau was so impressed he asked Boudreau where he got that.

"A genie gave me that. Just paddle around the bend there and you'll see a big rusty drum tied to a limb there. Just rub that drum and she will come out and grant you one wish."

Tibodeau hurry and paddle out there to get his wish. He was so nervous and excited. When he got there, he rub that drum and sure 'nuff, out she came.

"What is you wish master?" she asked. "Mais, let me see. Oh, yes! I want a million bucks."

"Your wish is on its way."

Sure enough. The sky fill up with ducks. All kinds of ducks. Big ones, 'lil ones - - all kinds. He was so upset. He didn't want ducks, so he paddled back to Boudreau. The ducks still following him. "Boudreau! What's the matter with 'dat dam genie. I ask for a million bucks and look what she send me."

"Don't feel too bad, Tibodeau...Do you think I ax for a 12 inch Bic lighter?"

GATOR SAUCE PIQUANT

2 pounds alligator meat cubes
2 cups chopped onions
⅓ cup cooking oil
½ cup chopped celery
¼ cup chopped bell pepper
¼ cup chopped shallots
¼ cup chopped parsley
2 (8 ounce) cans tomato sauce
1 can Ro-tel Tomatoes
2 Tablespoons Worcestershire Sauce
¼ teaspoon basil
1 bay leaf
¼ teaspoon oregano
Mushrooms, sliced
Salt and pepper to taste

Alligator may be marinated in wine for 1 hour before adding to
sauce. Saute onion in oil until a dark golden brown, stirring often.
Bell pepper and celery are then added and sauted until tender.
Add Ro-tel tomatoes and tomato sauce and seasonings, simmer
for 10 minutes, then add mushrooms and drained alligator meat.
Cover and cook for 40 minutes, add shallots and parsley and cook
uncovered for 4 minutes. Serve with rice.

DIRTY RICE

Melt shortening in large heavy Dutch oven. Add flour and stir until blended; then add sausage (cut into bite sized pieces) and bell pepper. Cook 5 minutes. Add shrimp, tomatoes, water, onions, garlic, and parsley. Bring to a boil; add rice; and stir in Worcestershire sauce, salt, thyme, and red pepper. Cover and simmer for 30 minutes, or until rice is tender. Stir occasionally. Sprinkle with parsley. Does not freeze well. Serves 8.

Typical South Louisiana dish.

1 Tablespoon shortening
2 Tablespoons flour
1 pound pure pork sausage, smoked, or loose uncased sausage
½ cup bell pepper, chopped
3 cups raw shrimp, peeled, deveined, and chopped
5 cups tomatoes, diced and peeled
2½ cups water
1 large onion, chopped
1 clove garlic, chopped
2 Tablespoons parsley, chopped
2 cups raw rice
2 Tablespoons Worcestershire sauce
1¼ teaspoons salt
½ teaspoon thyme
¼ teaspoon red pepper

Crawfish Boulettes (French Acadian)

1 lb. crawfish tails
1 bell pepper
2 eggs
1 T. Worcestershire sauce
Garlic powder
1 onion
1 C. seasoned breadcrumbs
Dark red pepper
Salt

Grind crawfish, onion, and bell pepper. Mix well with breadcrumbs, eggs, Worcestershire, salt and red pepper. Shape into balls. Roll in flour. Deep fat fry. Serve hot.